Contents

*S = silver; G = gold; P = platinum; ( ) = the line must be played but cannot be assessed for a Medal.

Let My People Go

Spiritual arr. Sarah Watts

Menuetto

from Symphony No. 25 in G minor, K. 183, third movement

Mozart arr. Sally Adams

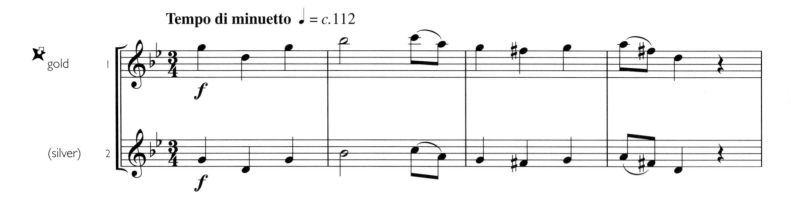

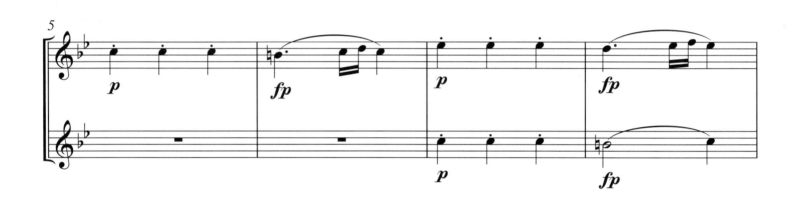

AB 3023

Short'nin' Bread

Trad. American arr. Gordon Lewin

AB 3023

Open Plains and Endless Skies

Sally Adams

Shalom Aleichum

Trad. Jewish arr. Gordon Lewin

AB 3023

Baroque-n Heart

Cecilia McDowall

March of the Tripoids

Colin Cowles

Tripoids is a made-up word meaning three-legged people.

AB 3023

A Happy and Harmonious Blacksmith

Air from Suite No. 5 in E, HWV 430, fourth movement

Handel arr. Colin Cowles

AB 3023

Penny Farthing

Gordon Lewin

AB 3023

The Heavenly Choir

Paul Harris

AB 3023

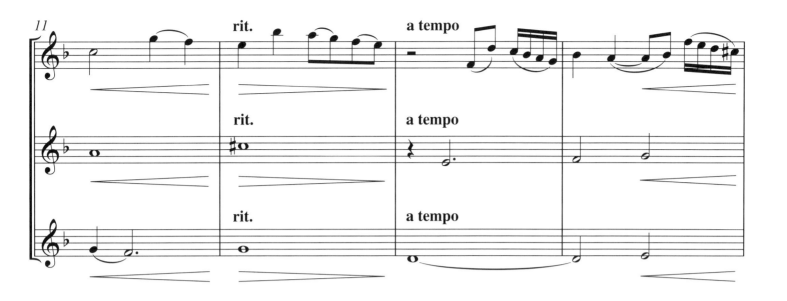

Bourée

Di Fabrio arr. Sally Adams

AB 3023

Barren Wasteland

Colin Cowles

AB 3023

Croissants and Coffee under the Eiffel Tower

Paul Harris

AB 3023

Suburban Blues

James Rae

AB 3023

Takes 4 2 Tango

Cecilia McDowall